JOHN DAVIES

A Source Book of Tractors and Farm Machinery

A Source Book of

Tractors and Farm Machinery

Richard Lee

First published in Great Britain in 1979 by Ward Lock Limited

This edition published in 2008 by Bounty Books,
a division of Octopus Publishing Group Ltd
2–4 Heron Quays, London E14 4JP
www.octopusbooks.co.uk

An Hachette Livre UK Company
www.hachettelivre.co.uk

ISBN: 978-0-753717-84-4

A CIP catalogue record for this book is available from the British Library

Printed and bound in China

ACKNOWLEDGMENTS

The author and publisher would like to express their thanks to the owners of photographs reproduced in this book:

Agricultural Machinery Journal; Agricultural Press (Farmers Weekly) Library; Amac; Bamfords; Bomford & Evershed; David Brown Tractors; Cantone; Claas; Ford Tractor Operations; Howard Machinery; R. A. Lister; Massey Ferguson; Mather & Platt; Ransomes Sims & Jefferies; Rasspe; Sperry New Holland; Taarup; and Vicon.

Jacket. British Leyland Synchro 462 tractor drawing heavy disc harrows.

Frontispiece. The end of the day and one of the famous Lockinge Shires is released from the cart and led back to its stable.

Contents page. Topping up the seed barrow.

CONTENTS

FOREWORD

The contents of this book are divided into two distinct halves. Part One covers the development of tractors and farm machines from their early days of commercial use until the 1960s. Although there was a considerable amount of steam technology and steam-powered equipment in use long before World War I, it was American War Aid that brought the Fordson tractor to Britain in 1919.

After World War II the uptake of farm machinery gathered pace and there was at this time an interesting period of development in the design of both tractors and agricultural machinery in general.

Machines in the last decade have become mostly redesigned to take into account more sophisticated farming methods as well as to make use of the much larger power supplies offered by tractor power drives and hydraulics. For this reason Part Two of this book gives typical examples of many machine types to become popular in the last ten years. As many as five hundred new machines arrive each year on the British market alone and as these are the machines that are in use today and can be seen working in fields, orchards and farmyards, rather more space has been devoted to showing the current technology than the earlier machines which now belong in the annals of industrial archaeology.

The historical first half is divided into two, 'Between the wars' and 'After World War II'. The pictures are presented in a generally chronological order to show the techniques in wide use at particular times.

The technical second half of the book is a summary of machines developed in the last decade. Its four sections cover general farming machines, modern tractors, specialized machines and self-propelled machines.

INTRODUCTION

Although tractors and farm machines (without which no modern country can grow its food) have a development history of eighty years or so, it is only in the last thirty years that they have established their acceptance commercially in Britain.

The evolution of commercial farm machinery really has its roots in American agriculture. American farmers were more willing to turn to mechanization and new methods of farming, hence they provided the demand for farm machines long before the European farmer. Between the wars American farmers were thirty years ahead of Europe in becoming mechanized. This disparity has now disappeared and it is the turn of developing countries to change their peasant farming into mechanized agriculture.

Countries like Spain and Portugal are fast catching up with modern techniques but there are many developing countries (such as parts of Africa, the Middle East and China) where agriculture still depends upon manual labour and animal power. These countries employ 75 per cent of their workforce simply growing food to live – with farm machinery this can be reduced to under 10 per cent. In this way farm machinery releases 65 per cent of the country's working population to concentrate on other tasks of modern civilization.

Loading peat into the cart for winter fuel on the Isle of Skye.

Evolution of farm machine design

The early machines were, of course, designed for use with horses and therefore ran off the power generated by the wheels of the machine or from an engine mounted on top. One of the earliest of harvest machines was the mower and this was followed by the reaper which would carry the cut crop to one side for labourers to parcel and tie in sheaves.

The invention of an automatic knotting device meant it became possible to build a binder which would parcel and tie its own sheaves. The power to operate the binder came from a 'drudge' or land wheel (situated under the corn elevator). Complicated mechanical drives took power from this wheel to oscillate the 1.4 m (4 ft 6 in) mower knife, to run the canvas belt conveyor and elevator, to turn the sails that led the crop on to the knife, to run the packing fingers that gathered the loose corn into a sheaf, and to trip and turn the knotting mechanism that tied a string around the sheaf centre when the packers were full. The ejected sheaves fell to the ground for labourers to stand in 'stooks' of eight or ten and would remain in the field for 'three church bells' or at least a fortnight before they would be dry enough to cart away and build into a corn stack in the farm rick-yard.

At first, then, most tractors were employed on straight draught or pulling work. For cultivations this involved pulling modified horse ploughs, disc harrows and seed drills which had had their shafts cut off and tractor drawbars fixed in their place. Implements of this nature were produced in purpose-built tractor forms but farmers were loath to buy expensive new machines when a conversion of the old horse implement seemed all that was necessary.

So, at first, tractors weren't generally required to do more than pull. But some models boasted a pulley wheel which would allow the tractor to act as a stationary power unit and, by means of long belts, drive tackle such as a thrashing machine or baler – machines which originally had been designed to work in conjunction with steam.

The Ferguson tractor

Although Harry Ferguson had designed his little grey tractor some years before World War II, it wasn't until the war was over that he was able to bring it into mass production in Britain. His tractor marked the opening of a new era in tractor and farm machinery design. It was fitted with a 3-point hydraulic lift linkage at the back which enabled implements to be suspended rather than simply pulled. This made the implements easier to construct and more efficient in work since they added their own weight to the tractor's rear wheels and gave them a better grip.

The tractor was also equipped with a power drive shaft, nowadays called a power take-off (pto) which would drive implements from the tractor's engine. Even more revolutionary was the external hydraulic pipeline on the tractor. This would fill the rams of a tipping trailer to unload at the touch of a lever. Later, in the 1970s, hydraulic energy would be incorporated into the design of nearly every implement.

Harvesting wheat in Kent, 1948.

Evolution between tractor and machine

All of Ferguson's ideas have since been adopted by every other tractor manufacturer in the world and the degree of power and control from the tractor has been extended and developed ever since.

This has meant a continuing evolution between tractor and machine. As the tractor has been improved, e.g. by greater engine power, so the implement maker has built his plough or cultivator that bit bigger to take advantage of the tractor's full potential. If a 50 hp tractor would pull discs with a 3 m (10 ft) working width, a 70 hp tractor needed discs spanning 4.5 m (15 ft) to consume the power. In this way the tractor would be able to complete a greater area per day to earn its keep.

Petrol and paraffin give way to diesel fuel

Development of the diesel engine suited to truck use was proceeding in parallel with the growing sophistication of the farm tractor but it wasn't until 1950 that self-starting diesel engines became generally available for farm tractors which had until then run either on petrol or, more commonly, petrol and paraffin. The tractors had to be started on petrol and switched to paraffin (more popularly called tractor vaporizing oil or 'tvo') when the engine had warmed up. Switching over too early caused incomplete vaporization of the fuel which made the engine smoke excessively, run with very low power and led to heavy cylinder bore wear and sump oil dilution. With petrol relatively expensive at the time, many farm workers would switch over early to 'help' the farmer. In reality many tractors had much shortened working lives as a result.

The diesel engine, with its noted economy, reliability and easier starting, has proved ideal for farm tractor power and now almost every tractor is powered by a diesel unit of one sort or another.

Looking at tractor and farm machine together

There are already many books which cover the different models and makes of old and vintage farm tractors but there are very few books which look at the various farm machines that have been made. This book is intended to look at both together, showing how an improvement in performance or capability in one has influenced the design of the next generation of the other.

It is hard to fully appreciate how suddenly the change to mechanized farming has come to Britain. In the span of thirty years we have seen the diesel tractor arrive and conquer the world market. We have seen farm mechanization develop to the extent

Breaking down the bracken to prepare the land for pasture.

that most of Britain's farms operate on the skeleton staff of one full-time man. Relatively few farms employ more than one worker, many are only part-time holdings for the farmer and his family.

More specialized farm machines have arrived, those that have their own power units and are self-propelled. The combine harvester is the best-known example of this class of machine. At first imported from America, the combine is now built in Britain at Kilmarnock, Scotland. Self-propelled machines now frequently seen include sugar beet harvesters, potato harvesters, pea and bean viners. Other self-propelled farm machines that are available and becoming more common are sprayers, grass foragers, irrigation machines and hay balers.

It must be appreciated that today the tractor is no longer a partner to many 'fixed' machines found on the farm. 'Fixed' or stationary equipment includes complex milking machinery and milk storage tanks, grain drying and storage facilities with automatic conveying, cattle feed towers that fill and empty automatically and feed milling and mixing installations that in many cases carry the finished feed to the pigs' mangers. These machines are usually powered by electric motor or in-built engine. Occasionally the tractor is used to drive a stand-by electricity generator or act as a stationary power unit, but the trend is for the tractor to do this in emergency only.

Browns' 'Buzzard' Flat-8 bale grab fitted to a Massey-Ferguson front loader.

Major farming changes created by mechanization

It will help in appraising the following photographs of farm machines if we can understand the other major changes that the advent of mechanized farming has brought about.

The greatest change is probably the vastly increased area of land that is now put under the plough every year. Before World War II when ploughing was done by horses, a farmer found he could only find time and power enough to till very little of his holding, the rest being what he called 'permanent pasture' or grass that grew well enough naturally. His arable fields would be tilled regularly in some sort of crop rotation.

With tractor power at beck and call, however, the modern farmer can decide today to plough a 4-hectare (10-acre) field and have it finished by tomorrow lunch-time. This enables him to carry far more arable fields than his father could, to plough up and re-seed his old pastures more frequently to keep them higher yielding, and to some extent redresses the annual land loss to urbanization and motorway building as the tractor is able to win back each year more 'fringe' land from moorland and otherwise uncultivated areas. Thanks to the tractor, the speed of field operations is such that weather risks at harvest time are lessened and control measures against pests and blight can be taken in good time.

Perhaps, however, the second most important result of tractor farming has been the practicability of silage-making that mechanization has made possible. Silage is the name for grass or green crops stored for cattle consumption. The technique simply requires a large mass of green matter to be compressed in a heap or tower. It will ferment and then keep in its own gases until opened up for feeding. It is more nutritious than hay and can be made in any weather, however wet.

More machinery has been devoted to silage-making than any other type of operation except, perhaps, tillage. This is because silage work demands speed at all stages – cutting the green crop, lifting and carting the crop after it has (usually) been allowed to wilt a little, loading the silage into its container or silo, and the cutting out and feeding of the resultant silage in the winter.

Silage is heavy stuff and cattle will eat from 22 kg (50 lb) of it per head per day. The mechanized handling of silage, as with all other farm crops, is almost a subject in itself. Some farmers have bought forklift trucks from factory warehouses and put them to work on the farm. Now the forklift truck manufacturers are building special rough-terrain models for the agricultural market. In this way we see the market evolving and the machines developing in response.

GLOSSARY

Artics – bend-in-the-middle.
Auger – corkscrew-type conveyor.
Balance or reversible plough – a plough with swing-over body to turn its furrows to right or left.
Cambridge ring roller – a roller which firms the seed-bed after sowing.
Clamp silage – silage formed in a heap and not in a tower.
Cleated – ridged.
Comecon – Communist trade community.
Contra-rotate – two discs circling in opposite directions.
Crown wheel – large drive wheel within a gearbox.
Crumbler – heavy circular cage to crush soil.
Cutterbar – portion of a mower which carries the knife.
Coulter – steel body that cuts the soil.
Derris – an insecticide.
Drawbar – hook on tractor or implement for attachment.
Drudge or land wheel – wheel that provides power to a towed implement by virtue of its contact with the ground.
Ensilage – preserving green matter in air-tight clamps for winter feed.
Epicyclic gear – an internal gearing arrangement.
Fingerbar mower – a mower that uses an oscillating knife.
Former – a forming mould.
Gin – an early engineering term for a machine worked by animal power.
Haulm – plant tops.
Headland – strips of a field used for turning the machine around and cultivated last of all.
Jerrican-style – in the shape of a petrol can.
Jig – framework that holds something in place during construction.
Mouldboard ploughing – to cultivate by inverting the soil.
pto – (tractor) power take-off.
Rams – pressurized pistons to lift or lower an attachment.

Rowcrop – crop grown in a row.
Seed fiddle – hand-held seed broadcaster.
Seed-hopper – tank that holds seed.
Shares – the replaceable wearing point of any soil-engaging tool.
Strakes – swing-out legs that lock out to give extra grip.
Swath – width of one sweep of a mower.
Tines – operating prongs of a machine, either rigid or flexible (spring-tines)
Torque – moment of force.
Trace elements – very small quantities of essential minerals.
Transponders – small radio transmitters.
Windrow – long row.
WLA – Women's Land Army.

Part One

Historical

BETWEEN THE WARS

Ploughing with horses

This combination of three horses and a single-furrow reversible (or 'balance') plough is somewhat unusual. More commonly two horses would pull a single-furrow mouldboard plough which would work the two sides of an ever-widening strip of ploughing. The balance plough tips over at the end of the furrow, however, to work back along the same length it has just completed, thus working steadily from one side of the field across to the other. Many English fields have one hedge that stretches a furlong or 'furrow-length' (200 m or 220 yd) and this was reckoned to be as far as a good team would pull a plough before needing a short rest.

Early horse-drawn reaper

An example of an early reaper built by McCormick in America, this early print clearly shows the drudge or land wheel providing the power to turn the sails and lift the retaining rake at regular intervals. The cutterbar knife will be driven by the inner cog-wheel. The artist has shown the cut corn batches as being laid across the reaper's line of travel whereas the mechanism would seem to be ejecting the batches in direct line of travel with the corn heads laid to the rear.

Horse-drawn mower

Although lacking its shafts, this well-preserved Hornsby mower shows how the drive is taken from an epicyclic gear within the drudge wheel to a bevel gear within the gearbox to turn the crank that oscillates the knife with triangular sections. These sections, producing a scissor-like cutting action between the fixed cutterbar fingers, are made of high carbon steel and can be sharpened or replaced when blunt or broken.

Farm wagons

These were the combined work of several craftsmen – joiner, blacksmith and wheelwright. Costing between £20 to £40 at the turn of the century, wagons would last fifty years or more. Different timbers were needed for different parts – the wheel hubs (hardness), wheel spokes (springiness), wheel rims (non-warping), etc. A steel tyre was heated and shrunk on to each wheel. Loose racks would slot into the cart fore and aft to hold loads of loose hay or corn sheaves. Names for the different parts of a horse wagon vary according to area.

Horses sweeping hay

In the late nineteenth century the introduction of hay-lifting tackle and the elevator made rick building a much faster process. If the rick was built in the same field that the hay was cut, then it could be swept to the rick site by a giant comb or sweep instead of hand-loading haycarts with pitchforks.

Most sweeps were of the one-horse type. This one, pulled by two horses, could gather a larger load and had power to spare to give the farm-hand a ride. To discharge the load, a side chain to each horse was unhitched to let the horses turn right round and withdraw the sweep from under its load of hay.

The elevator (left)

Although most elevators were powered by small stationary petrol engines, even from very early times, this rare picture shows an elevator driven by a horse-powered gin. The horse is out of the picture but the central crown wheel it is turning can be seen. It drives a cog and shaft leading to the elevator. The shaft has a universal joint at mid-point, just past the place where the horse must step over it on each circuit.

Trussing hay

Hay that had fully dried and matured in the stack would often be sold 'by the truss'. Cutting the rick up into neat bundles which would be tied by string was a skilled job often done on piece-work by a senior man. The hay knife, a broad flat blade running to a point, would be worked up and down to cut out a block-shaped truss of hay weighing about 25 kg (56 lb). The iron spike, pushed down through the truss, held it together and tipped it while the strings were tied.

A thrashing team

During the late nineteenth and early twentieth century contractors with steam engines and heavy tackle would tour farms to work on piece-rate. Here the team consists of a Ransomes 7 hp traction engine, a thrashing machine with 1.4 m (54 in) wide drum, and a chaff cutter chopping up the threshed straw as it is discharged from the thresher. Note the large sacks of wheat that would weigh 127 kg (20 stones) when full (now outlawed but one man had to carry them in those days), also the axle jack set under the steam engine's rear wheel – set thus to hold the engine steady and to tighten the driving belt to the drum.

Austin tractor of 1919

From 1900 onwards many engineering companies plus quite a few inventors produced tractors in small quantities. The food effort of World War I motivated many companies into tractor production. This Austin tractor had a 25 hp 4-cylinder side-valve paraffin engine. The tractor weighed 1,500 kg (1½ tons) and cost £300 with independent rear wheel brakes.

Fiat Model 702 tractor (1919)

This was the first farm tractor built by Fiat (now a leading builder and supplier of tractors). This machine actually competed in what was probably Britain's first tractor trial held in Lincoln on 24 September 1919. With 4-cylinder paraffin engine developing 18–25 hp, the tractor weighed about 2,800 kg (2.8 tons). Note that all these early tractors had iron wheels front and rear.

Fordson Standard N tractor (1919)

The most successful of all the early tractor designs, this Standard Fordson (in various models) was still popular during World War II. The Ford Motor Co. (who could not call its tractors 'Ford' for many years because there was another American tractor company also called Ford) appointed a network of dealers across Britain to sell its tractors. Good service and after-sales back-up has kept Ford tractors a leading British make and top seller during the late 1970s. In 1977 alone Britain's farmers bought 33,000 tractors.

The Howard Rotavator

A. C. Howard invented the rotary cultivator in Australia in 1922. He became a joint founder of the international farm machinery company Rotary Hoes Ltd, now renamed Howard Machinery Ltd. This company also built tractors for a time. The picture shows A. C. Howard driving a 1932 Howard DH22 tractor with 1 m (3 ft) wide heavy-duty Rotavator attached which had been working for thirty-seven years on a Queensland sugar cane estate. This picture was taken in 1969 only eighteen months before A. C. Howard died at the age of seventy-seven.

The pre-war Ferguson

Harry Ferguson was only able to get his model tractor into limited production in 1935. At first he joined forces with the David Brown tractor company which produced a joint-effort model until World War II halted production. The picture shows it hauling a then-modern binder. The binder operator has controls to raise or lower the sail according to the height of the corn, to see the string band is tied centrally on the sheaf, and to raise or lower the cutterbar's cutting height to clear any bottom weed growth. A tied sheaf is just being ejected by the knotter.

Horse-drawn side rake for hay

A simple machine of four combs between two discs to rake two swaths of hay into one larger windrow for the sweep. By removing a centre section from each of the combs, the machine would act as a swath turner, turning two swaths of drying grass at one pass.

Tractor sweeping hay

A Standard Fordson on rubbers pushing the sweep. Some sweeps ran on two small wheels and driving involved the art of 'kinking' the sweep in the opposite direction you wanted to turn to, and then 'following it around'. Tractors with rubber tyres appeared about 1930 but steel wheels were common up to 1947 due to the wartime shortage of rubber.

The hay loader (right)

Making hay has always been a race against the weather. This Knapps Patent loader provoked controversy as it was thought to encourage the farmer to carry hay before it was fully dry but it also saved much hand labour when loads of hay had to be carted out of the field.

Cocked hay (left)

In wet districts it was the custom to build hay into small temporary ricks or cocks to mature in the fields, their thatched-type construction causing them to shed any rain. By attaching a cage to a hay loader, one man stacking could build a haycock. When the cage was full he tripped the latch and swung the cage over to leave a finished haycock standing in the field.

Carrying in the haycocks

This haycock trailer was invented by a farmer named William T. Todd. Slats between chains driven by the tractor's power take-off (pto) enabled it to wind on up to three haycocks each weighing 500 kg (10 cwt). In Ireland farmers used tractors with linkage-mounted buckrakes (see page **61**) to carry in the haycocks. The traditional ways of making hay persisted long after the introduction of modern tractors.

Binding sheaves and stacking stooks

Three horses haul a binder while labourers build the tied sheaves in 'shocks' or 'stooks', usually eight or ten sheaves to a stook. It really depended on how thick the crop was – if the sheaves fell close together you put ten to a stook, if the crop was light you had less wasted walking to build them in eights. Although the combine harvester had progressed to self-propelled models in America, this '1920 method' was still a common sight at the time of this photograph in 1939.

Thrashing and baling

Thrashing from the wagon – in this case a crop of Cocksfoot grass that has been cut for seed and has been matured in stooks of sheaves in the field. The horse doesn't get a rest, he is hitched into another cart now loading to replace the one being unloaded. A very dusty job, the drum 'feeder' has erected a tarpaulin around himself to reduce the wind. The threshed Cocksfoot straw is being baled by a wire-tying Bowell stationary baler. The man on this side inserts iron needles between ram strokes to divide the bales and inserts a length of wire. An operator on the other side feeds the wires back through grooves in the next needle and the first man then twists the ends together. The bales could weigh 100 kg (2 cwt) or more and the trick in making the rick was to let the baler shove the bales up a ladder or inclined plank.

Baling barley straw (left)
Again using a stationary baler, driven here by crossed belt (to reverse the direction of drive) to the pulley of a Fordson E27N. The foreman is just pushing a needle home while a spare needle stands against the baler wheel. This needle has just been placed there by the young man now taking off the bale. For some reason they are not building a rick of bales as the roller-conveyor is not being used. Maybe the straw is being loaded on to a lorry for direct sale. Although typical of a wartime baling operation, this picture is in fact dated 1953.

Bagger-type Holt combine (below)
Thought to be imported from America about 1930, this Holt combine harvester drawn by a Caterpillar tractor would have created quite a stir for several years. It is interesting to note that Holt's called the machine a 'combined harvester' – the correct description as it combines the tasks of cutting the corn and theshing it into one operation. Just when the word 'combine' arrived is not entirely clear. However, with the accent firmly on the first syllable, it is the job of combining that is carried out today.

American combine harvester

This trailed combine harvester had its own engine and featured a grain hopper. Imported to a Suffolk farm in 1936 it made headlines because with it two men could harvest 16 ha (40 acres) of corn in a day. Output on this scale was quite unheard of at that time. The pulling tractor is a single-cylinder German Lanz 'Bulldog'. Running on heavy oil, it developed 30 hp. Lanz tractors were imported from the late 1920s by the Locomobile Engineering Co. of London.

The Land Army ploughs for victory

The Women's Land Army, recruited to combat the shortage of farm workers, was soon at home with the latest machinery. Here driving Standard Fordsons, two WLA girls haul 2-furrow and 3-furrow Ransomes ploughs. The trailed multi-body plough was very popular. The hand controls which could be adjusted on-the-go comprised a winding handle to drop the plough in deeper or lift it up to plough shallower, to lift and set levers to vary the front furrow width and tilt of the plough frame, and a trip lever that dropped a toothed sector on to the toothed hub of the land wheel. This would lift the plough out of work into a locked raised position at the end of the furrow length while turning to set back into work on the return run. A second pull on the trip lever dropped the plough back into its working position. This piece of ploughing, however, looks rather too expert for two such recently-recruited young farm-hands!

Sowing by seed fiddle

Something like a cross between bagpipes and violin, the bow spins a disc on to which seed falls. Vanes on the disc throw the seed out in an arc to broadcast the seed evenly. Seed scattered on plough furrows would be covered by a flat beam harrow dragged over the field. Breaking down the plough furrow tops, this would scrape most of the seed into the valleys – leaving it to come up in rows. Note how the seed fiddle is the forerunner of the tractor broadcaster (see page **65**).

Sowing by seed barrow (centre of picture)

Drive from the single wheel oscillates a distributor mechanism along the bottom of the seed hopper. Seed barrows were used to sow corn and grass seeds. Here it is almost certainly grass that is being sown and quite likely the farmer at the handles – most workmen were expected to push the barrow unaided! The tractor on the left harrows in the seed already sown while the other is sowing artificial fertilizer in advance from a wide 'dribbler' type distributor.

Mechanized sowing

Now the seed barrow body has been put on to the back of a tractor. The barrow wheel is gone and drive is taken from the tractor pto by simple sprockets and chain (no doubt from a bicycle). The drawbar shows the hitch of a following implement, most likely a Cambridge ring roller followed by a light harrow trailing behind. Seeds sown and covered in one pass from the tractor seat!

Sowing sugar beet seeds in rows

When the seeds germinate they will have to be hand-thinned, then hand-singled and always kept hoed. If the rows can be kept straight at least the straight hoeing can be done by horse hoe. The horse is being led by an unseen person on its near side. He is taking the 4-row drill back on its own mark, the wheel track falling just within the last wheelmark. The seed is metered out by revolving cup wheels (similar to a water wheel) driven by the land wheel. Pressing the bar either side disconnects this drive and stops the sowing action (as when turning at the headland).

End of World War II

This symbolic picture of a Bren gun carrier drilling oats with a Massey Harris combine drill (seed plus fertilizer) epitomized the great shortage of farm machinery and the hope for mechanized farming in the future. However, petrol rationing which continued after the war made it uneconomic to turn many tanks into tractors!

Cutting hay

The converted horse mower has two handles for the rider to mind – one to engage drive to the knife, the other to lift the cutterbar clear on the corners. The stick (held by the man at the back) is to tease out any clumps in this heavy crop. The tractor is a later model of the Ransomes crawler that was first produced in 1936 and remained in production for over twenty years. The photograph was taken about 1949 and was a publicity picture for a firm of seed merchants in Chester – hence the suit and tie worn by the driver!

Raking and rowing the new way

One of the first examples of putting a rotary action to use instead of a reciprocating motion, the spring-tine hay turner worked from friction with the ground. At first a trailed machine, the wheels to each swath could be set to turn each swath separately or to rake two rows into one large windrow for baling. Later as a mounted rake, the Vicon Acrobat hay rake became one of the most widely-owned and popular post-war machines.

Silage-making

Only the scientists understood the process of ensilage – preserving green matter for cattle feed in air-tight clamps. Here Women's Land Army girls pack sugar beet tops into a cheap silo made from chestnut fencing and a liner. The author even acted a small part in a Ministry of Information film at that time (1939) called *Mr Borland Thinks Again* – which told of a farmer deciding to give silage-making a try.

A new invention to harvest standing corn

Designed in 1947 by two famous British pioneer agricultural engineers, D. R. Bomford and F. W. McConnel, the Wild Harvester had only two moving parts, knocking and sucking the grain from the ears of the standing corn as it passed over. The blast was directed into two cyclones which blew the light chaff out while the heavier corn was flung to the outside and fell into collecting troughs leading to the bagging spouts. The straw left could then be cut and tied for thatching. The Wild Harvest Thresher, however, failed to become a commercial success.

Early use of chemical sprays

Spraying dilute sulphuric acid on potatoes to kill the haulm prior to lifting the crop. Although merely a barrel mounted on shafts and iron wheels, this machine is a proprietary make. The barrel was filled by a rotary hand lever pump at the front left while drive from the offside wheel to a pump kept the boom jets supplied. The most modern feature of this sprayer was that the nearside wheel could adjust its track on release of a locking bolt in order to match the row widths.

Spreading chemicals in earnest
This Allman Pestmaster powder duster is probably spreading derris. Priced at £95 in 1948, the Pestmaster was self-propelled, power-operated by its 2¼ hp engine and had a 2.5 m (8 ft) dusting boom. It also had wheels that were adjustable for rowcrop work.

Hand-dusting against Colorado beetle
Dusting DDT by hand blower on to emerging potato plants after a Colorado beetle scare. Illustrated posters offering cash rewards to anyone finding a Colorado beetle (a notifiable pest since 1877) meant that this foreign insect was better known than the British wireworm!

The grey 'Fergie'

Now in a smart grey livery and with neater lines, more than half a million of these popular tractors were built from 1946 onwards at the Coventry factory. This tractor was the turning point of British tractor design. Harry Ferguson obtained his first concept of the tractor in World War I, showed it to Ford and other manufacturers but built his first prototype in 1933. In 1936 he joined with David Brown who built 1,250. Ferguson left the David Brown company which wanted to build a more powerful tractor, and went back to Ford who built 300,000 9N tractors in Detroit from 1939 to 1947. Ferguson fell out with Ford and found the Standard Motor Company of Coventry willing to build the TE20 (Tractor England) model at the Banner Lane plant. Ferguson is said to have been awarded $9,250,000 damages in a legal action against Ford for using his designs.

Planting potatoes sitting down (left)

This 2-row potato planter is fitted to the tractor's 3-point linkage and can be lifted clear of the ground by the driver at the touch of a lever. Disc coulters open a furrow, the seed potato is dropped and two discs close earth back over the seed and build its ridge. The dropping mechanism is simply a moving tray with compartments that tip the seed into its dropping spout. The moving tray is driven by chain from the outside hub of the offside land wheel. The hopper in front of the potato platform hold artificial fertilizer which is metered out by a simple mechanism working off the same drive.

Hoeing rowcrops by tractor (right)

This rowcrop hoe carried on the 3-point linkage of a Ferguson TE20 has been adapted to precision work by fitting a seat and inserting a length of pipe by which the operator can keep the hoe working close to the plants (probably kale) without cutting them out, even if the tractor driver has let his steering wander an inch or two!

DAVID BROWN

Specialist rowcrop tractor (left)

This David Brown 2D rowcrop tractor had a very economical 14 hp 2-cylinder diesel engine and mid-mounted tool frame with pneumatic lift to give the driver a close view and good control of his row-crop operation. Here he is earthing up potato ridges, a job that reduces weed and the number of greened potatoes in one pass. A rear lift and pto were optional but it didn't find a large market. Only 2,000 were made between 1956 and 1961.

Potato elevator-digger at work (right)

Lifting two rows of potatoes at a time especially after the haulm have been killed off by spraying with dilute sulphuric acid, the potatoes are returned to lie on the top of the ground to dry out for a short while before the hand pickers collect them into baskets.

Harvesting potatoes by spinner
A simple machine for revealing the potatoes is the spinner which simply scatters the ridge to one side by means of raking tines set in a power-driven reel. This crop had been left in the ground throughout the winter and still yielded 25 tonnes per hectare (10 tons an acre) of good quality.

Lifting potatoes by manned harvester

Ransomes Faun harvester lifts one row at a time (by tractor offside wheel) and takes crop and soil up transversely to the tractor, to be sifted through the mesh of the elevating web and discharged on to the sorting table. Three pickers lift out the trash as the crop proceeds to the loading elevator that is discharging into the side-running trailer alongside.

Massey Harris 21 combine harvester

This Canadian-type self-propelled harvester with 3.5 m (12 ft) width of cut and 2,000 litre (60 bushel) grain tank was powered by 58 hp petrol Chrysler engine and cost £810 in 1943. It is important to appreciate that normal North American harvesting practice is to cut the corn and row it up with a mower/swather. It is left to dry out for a few days and then fleets of combine harvesters (usually operated by contract gangs) will move in to pick up and thresh the cut corn. Because American combines didn't have to contend with cutting the corn as well as threshing it, they were 'harvesters' rather than 'combined' or combine harvesters. It also meant they could work faster and with less risk of blockages or breakdowns.

David Brown Albion trailed combine

This bagger combine cutting only about 1.5 m (5 ft) width and its mechanism driven by pto from the tractor, was only one of many farm machines at one time made by the David Brown company. The name Albion came from a David Brown acquisition of Harrison, McGregor & Guest Ltd (this company is thought to have made almost a quarter of a million Albion mowers).

Tractor-mounted fingerbar mower

Little changed in basic design, the tractor fingerbar mower could be found in semi-mounted, fully rear-mounted and mid-mounted versions. Driven by the pto, the mower was slung on to the linkage arms which lifted the cutterbar clear on the corners at the touch of a lever. For transport the cutterbar was pegged into an upright position (as it had been with the horse-drawn versions).

Silage by buckrake

This was an immensely popular method started by progressive farmer Rex Paterson. Linkage-mounted buckrakes could be used for bringing in cocks of hay or, as Paterson discovered, for collecting freshly mown grass for silage. It simply needed the driver to reverse down a swath of mown grass to collect up to 500 kg (10 cwt) on the buckrake tines. This could be lifted and carted to the silo or clamp and dumped without leaving the tractor seat. The Bamfords S7 buckrake shown is of the later improved push-off type which shoves its load off by means of a moving back gate. Powered by hydraulic ram, the gate is returned to its first position by a powerful spring.

The silage clamp

Made between two walls, usually outdoors but here shown inside, and covered by plastic sheeting. The grass turns a rich tobacco colour and ferments to give off a distinctive smell. Cattle like it, however, and milk well on it during the winter. The problem is to find ways of cutting and feeding out clamp silage as it binds into a hard solid mass. A self-feeding rail like this permits the cattle to eat their way into the stack without waste. As they eat into it, the pipe barrier is moved up and secured.

Cattle self-feeding silage

This shows the self-feed barrier in action. Also visible are the cows' identity collars which carry transponders that enable electronic feeders to identify them and give them individual rations of concentrates.

Zetor 6718 tractor with chisel plough

This Czech tractor is working a Bomford Superflow chisel cultivator in the soil. With forward-angled chisel points on each tine, the cultivator points create a 'soil-boiling' action that breaks the ground before the legs meet the solid earth and thus reduce much of the resistance and the power needed to pull it. Faster than mouldboard ploughing, more farmers are turning to chisel-type cultivations instead of inverting the soil.

The Zetor tractor is one of many types now built in Communist-bloc countries. Others are the Belarus (Russia), Fortschritt (GDR), Ursus (Poland), Universal (Romania) and IMT (Yugoslavia).

Part Two

Technical

Tractor-mounted broadcaster

Probably the most popular post-war farm implement, the 'spinning disc' fertilizer spreader was first built in a 2-wheel trailed version that was driven by its own wheels and pulled behind the trailer stacked with bags of fertilizer. The width of spread was limited due to the relatively slow speed of the spinning disc, however, and this method tied up a second man on the trailer keeping the hopper filled. The mounted version with spinner driven by pto could hold up to 300 kg (6 cwt) of fertilizer and spread up to 9 m (30 ft) wide to discharge its load in less than ten minutes. On average every farmer in Britain bought a new spreader every five years and the best-known manufacturers were Teagle (one of the originators), Vicon and Reco.

EUROSPAND
S 500
MIL
WOLVERHAMPTON

The rotary cultivator

This is another popular machine to have been much copied after its patent protection ran out. Originally invented by Howard, the notion of tilling land by means of power-driven chopping blades has been taken up by manufacturers in nearly every country in Europe. A natural use for the tractor pto drive, rotary cultivators were the start of an evolution of powered tillage tools that went on to powered harrows with reciprocating tines, powered cultivators with a stirring action, and eventually machines offering a combination of treatments. The biggest variety are to be seen in Italy but other early manufacturers are the French Kuhn company and the W. German Krone company. Shown is the Irish Agrotiller, no longer made.

Farmyard manure side-spreader

Farmyard manure (which became known as FYM during World War II) was being spread by manure spreaders of the self-unloading trailer with rear beaters type which had made the predictable development from being ground-wheel driven (tremendous torque and strain on engagement) to being pto-driven. Then the side-spreader was invented by John Deere and manufactured under licence by Howard Rotavator. This open-top round tank discharged its load by means of a central pto-driven chain-loaded shaft which simply whipped the contents overboard. Having the advantage of carrying sloppy manure as well as solid, it became a best-seller. When the patent expired in Britain in 1976 (patents only last for fifteen years) other manufacturers started making side-spreaders – like the Hillman shown. At least ten different makes are on sale today.

Modern plough design

Despite many farmers turning away from mouldboard ploughing to chisel ploughing, rotary cultivation, and even no-tillage chemical techniques, the ever-increasing amount of land being put under cultivation each year has provided a ready market for all tillage manufacturers. Plough makers (famous names are Ransomes of Britain, Huard of France, Lemken of W. Germany, Kvernelands of Norway, Sanderum of Sweden) continued to develop plough design. Here shown is Ransomes 6-furrow semi-mounted plough. It tills such a wide swath that the tractor, in order to retain a central pull, can no longer drive with one wheel following the last furrow. The plough is too heavy for the 3-point hydraulic linkage to lift out of work (to do so would simply pick the tractor front wheels up on a see-saw effect) so the tractor hydraulics are used to raise the plough chassis at the front and to raise the plough rear on its trailing wheel by means of simultaneous hydraulic ram. Semi-mounted ploughs are made up to 12-furrows and in turn-over reversible models as well by firms such as Rabewerk (W. Germany).

Chisel ploughing by articulated tractor

Greater power offered by the new-style 4-wheel-drive, articulated steer tractors gives the chisel plough manufacturer the chance to build wider, faster working tools. This Bomford Powertrak (based on the Superflow see page **63**) uses all the 150 hp of the MF 1505 artic tractor pulling it. The Powertrak cultivator is lifted out of work by a hydraulic ram on each side that presses the pneumatic-tyred depth wheels down into the machine's transport position.

Working down a seed-bed

Using a combination of finishing implements, the tractor breaks the top inches into the finest of tilths ready for drilling with seed. The tractor (equipped with cage wheels to add grip and lessen ground pressure and compaction at the same time) is pulling a Doublet Record harrow fitted with a rolling cage crumbler and behind which is trailed a Canadian Flexicoil land packer which acts rather like a Cambridge roller.

Accurate spreading of artificial fertilizers

This Vicon spreader is made under licence to Alpha-Accord, the W. German company which pioneered air-blast spreading of fertilizers and seeds. By metering a flow of material into an air-stream and then dividing the airflow between delivery pipes, the machine achieves a very accurate and even distribution of material. This became important with the rising price of fertilizer and the introduction of 'tram-line' husbandry techniques (see page **73**).

A grain drill at work

Sowing corn with a Danish Nordsten drill imported by Ransomes. This drill is a combine drill and meters artificial fertilizer down the seed spouts. It is also a cultivator-type drill which cuts the seed furrow with a boot coulter – the other types have disc coulters to open the seed groove. Note the outrigger markers in action, the one on the left of the picture making a mark where the tractor front wheel must run next time. Rams to the rubber-tyred wheels lift the drill out of work and disengage the metering drive.

Tram-lining

The tractor wheelings running through standing crops are called 'tram-lines' and are laid down when the crop is sown. Thereafter the tractor follows the same wheelmarks whenever it enters the crop to carry out weeding, spreading fertilizers or spraying against weeds, insects or spore-bound diseases. The driver is hoeing seedlings that have just emerged and his front-mounted Steketee hoe reaches exactly half-way across to the next set of tram-lines. In the same way the farmer needs his fertilizer spreader and sprayer boom to be exactly matched to the tram-line widths.

The tractor is an Italian Same Saturno. Front-mounting of implements is still considered an ultra-modern concept; theoretically a tractor can operate one implement on the front and a second on the back at the same time. Lifting of this hoe is carried out by ram under the front-mounting base.

County
County

Sprayer for tram-line crops (left)

This Dorman sprayer carried on a high-clearance County tractor is kitted out for tram-line crops. Carrying extra chemical in its saddle tanks as well as its main rear tank, it can cover extra ground without leaving the field to replenish. The high clearance body enables it to work in growing crops without damaging the plants and the narrow rowcrop rear wheels (in line with the front wheels) mean it can keep exactly to the tram-lines.

Direct drilling into slits (right)

The practice of direct drilling seeds into slits is doing away with tillage cultivations altogether. Top grass or weed is killed off by spray while a special drill with sharp disc coulters cuts slits and drops in either grass, kale or cereal seed. Artificial fertilizers can also be sown into these slits at the same time. Direct drill pioneers are Bettinson and Moore and it is a Moore Uni-drill shown in the picture.

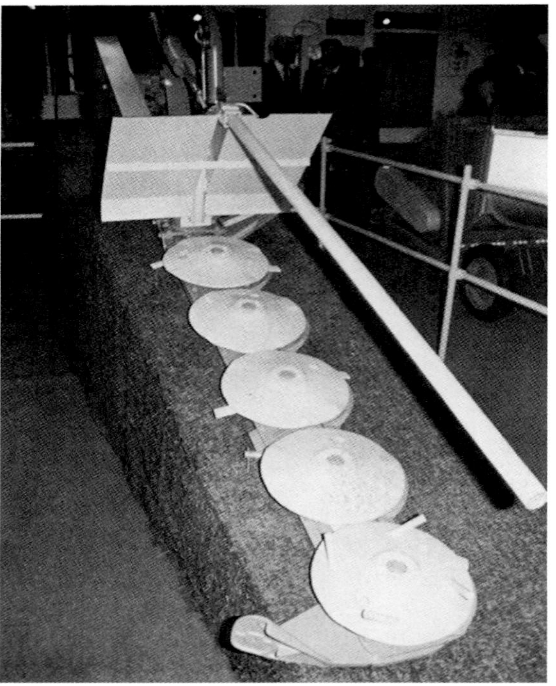

Rotary-action disc mower (left)

The fingerbar mower with its reciprocating knife lasted a long time but eventually succumbed to machines working on a rotary principle. The first rotary mowers were the pto-driven disc-type which had from four to six fast-spinning discs mounted on the mower bed. Each disc had two or three simple swinging knife sections on its perimeter and all discs (driven by a gear train in the mower bed) turn in the same direction (anti-clockwise as you look down on them). This disc mower by the French company Faucheux is without cover, shield or swathboard to show the basic construction.

Top-driven drum mowers (right)

The biggest selling type of rotary mower, however, proved to be the top-driven drum type which mostly do not have a bottom 'bed'. Most are built under licence from the Dutch company P. Zweegers or the W. German company Fahr. The drums contra-rotate to deliver a swath of mown grass between each pair. Blades are simply replaced by prising the covers apart and latching a new one in. The top drive is by vee-belt so repairs tend to be simple and maintenance costs low.

RASSPE
RASSPE
GT 2000

Loader-wagon for silage-making

Continental farmers use over 100,000 loader-wagons like this Claas LWU model. It picks up cut grass and chops it as it is elevated into the wagon body which has a moving floor to unload and discharge to rear or either side as and when required. This makes one-man silage-making almost fully mechanized but this system has never really caught on in Britain.

Baling hay and loading automatically
Early Russian Belarus tractor (but note compressed air tank for air brakes) pulls an E. German Fortschritt low-density baler. Making floppy bundles of hay, each one is catapulted on to the trailer behind when it enters the running bands of the bale thrower. The trailer is filled by random placement and is tipped to discharge. Low-density balers were first made in Germany about 1930 by Lanz and Welger. They use binder grade twine which is relatively cheap and the soft bales tend to breathe and cure into high quality hay. Low-density hay baling has never been very popular in Britain.

High-density baling of hay

Making neat square bales and packing the hay through at up to 10,000 kg (10 tons) an hour, the modern hay baler ties two strong sisal or polypropylene cords around each bale. The knotting mechanism is simply a stronger version of the knotter that was invented for the binder. In Spain many balers have a chopping mechanism in the intake when baling straw to chop it into chaff, and tie with three strings instead of two. It is also possible to equip a high-density baler with a wire tying mechanism if desired.

The New Holland 370 Hayliner picks up the crop by pick-up reel, feeds it into the bale chamber by flow-forking action, compresses the hay by a ram carriage travelling at eighty strokes a minute, and ties by a needle that carries the string up to the knotters on a ram back-stroke. On ejection the bale expands from its compression to tighten the strings.

Automatic bale collection

Rain spoils all hay, whether loose or in small or large bales. Once hay is baled it should be put under cover without delay. Many gadgets have been invented to load bales on to the trailer – this type of travelling elevator, the rising chain driven by its wheels, is commonly seen on the Continent.

Self-loading bale wagon

Taking both power drive and hydraulic power from the tractor, this bale wagon picks up bales by its collector chute which sends them up to a packing platform in front of the wagon. On the platform the bales get arranged in a flat layer of eight. When this is done the platform swings up to pack them as a 'wall' on to the trailer floor and pushes the existing load back by that distance. When the trailer has eleven rows it is full and will unload and discharge bales one at a time in roughly the opposite manner. Although solving the problem with interesting technology, the bale wagon is expensive in terms of capital outlay for a problem that exists on most farms for only a few days a year. The bale wagon has no other function.

Large round bales of hay and straw

Machines that roll hay or straw into round bales weighing up to 500 kg (10 cwt) have come to Europe from America during the 1970s. Farmers bought them eagerly at first because they promised an even quicker way to make hay. But handling the bales must be done mechanically and this has limited the further uptake of big bale haymaking. Many roll balers use running belts to make the bale rather like a giant cigarette rolling machine. The Claas roll baler uses perforated metal rollers, however. None use a knotter, binder twine is simply wound around a number of times and left with loose ends hanging that have to be tied by hand.

Loading big bales mechanically

The US Farmhand company designed this 3-bale mover to speed up bale collection. Moving trailer floor chains take the bales to the rear for unloading while a pair of forklift-type tines scoop up and load any bale the trailer is driven at.

Removing stones from potato land

Stones are the single biggest cause of machinery damage and breakdown. New thinking in potato growing is to put the stones into a layer below the ridges where the potatoes are grown as with the Reekie machine, or to put them to one side. In some cases a potato harvester is set to pick up the stones. The advantages to crop quality and more automated harvesting are such that we can expect to see stone removal become more extensively practised.

Automatic potato planting (below)

Similar to the 2-row planter on page **52**, the only difference with the Mil shown in the picture is that it uses a disc wheel of gripper fingers to grab and carry the seed potatoes over to the dropping point at the front. The hoppers will adjust for width of row and the planter will adjust for distance between each seed dropped. Mil is a British company, the circular gripper idea originated in Czechoslovakia.

Harvesting potatoes by teamwork (right)

Three tractors draw Ransomes-Johnson 2-row elevator diggers, two of which have cross conveyors to deliver left and right respectively. This means the three machines can leave the crop from six rows in one row. A Johnson lifter/loader follows on when the potatoes have dried off and loads the crop into a side-running trailer which will take the crop into store or to be graded and bagged for market.

HJL620

Dutch Amac D2/R36 root lifter

This unmanned trailed machine is shown harvesting carrots but it is also capable of lifting potatoes.

Self-propelled potato harvester

This W. German Hassia 2-row potato lifter has its own engine and does not need a tractor to pull it. It is shown here with a rear elevator that discharges into a side-running trailer but the machine can also be fitted with its own bulk tank to hold up to 3,000 kg (3 tons) of potatoes before discharging automatically.

Precision drilling sugar beet

Shortages during World War II encouraged the making of sugar from homegrown beet and factories which process beet have been in operation ever since. Sugar beet once required a great deal of hand labour, especially in singling and hoeing the crop. Now monogerm (single-plant) seed is spaced accurately by this Stanhay precision planter and little, if any, hand singling is needed. Note the small covering discs and press wheels which firm the seed into its bed.

Automatic harvesting of sugar beet (left)

This Catchpole Powerbeet single-row self-propelled beet harvester first slices the beet top off, then has a digger share that leads the beet on to the main elevator up to the tank. When the tank is full, the driver can empty it (in less than two minutes by elevator) into a side running trailer.

Note that this machine is powered by the engine and transmission of a Ford 4000 tractor. A tractor engine used in this way is called a 'skid unit'. In this case the wheels can be taken off the harvester and restored to make the tractor whole and independent when the beet harvest is over.

Giant 6-row beet harvester (right)

This French Herriau purpose-built harvester has a front-mounted flail-type topper that removes the leaves. Knife blades to each row slice the beet crowns off and digger shares lift the roots on to spider-wheel cleaning cages that work the beet to the rear of the machine where an elevator takes the crop up to the holding tank that will take 6–7,000 kg (6 or 7 tons) before having to discharge. On the Continent such machines are often owned by the beet factories which harvest the crops grown for them on contract by the local farmers.

LYNKON
484

Front loader attachments (left)

Playing an important part in reducing labour needed when loading manure, tearing out silage, loading loose beet into lorries, picking up big bales of hay or straw, digging, shifting or moving any heavy object, the tractor front end loader is one of the most popular accessories. This model is by Grays of Fetterangus and it is fitted to an IH 484 tractor.

Tipping trailers (right)

The geometry of the farm trailer is almost a study in itself. Most still use Ferguson's principle of placing the wheels at the rear to throw as much weight forward on to the tractor's rear wheels. Also like the Ferguson trailer, most are tippers but there are many chassis geometries used in trailers today. This scissor-lift tipper is useful because it can discharge its 6,000 kg (6 ton) load over a 2.5 m (8 ft) wall or into a silo or bin of that height. It will also tip at its lower chassis level or remain level when lifted. This could make it useful as a platform when painting a building, for instance. Some trailers have such large rams that they would need more oil to tip them than the tractor carries in its system. So these have their own reservoirs of oil and hydraulic pump powered by pto-drive from the tractor.

The stationary elevator

Clearly developed from the original hay and sheaf elevator used to build ricks, later adapted to lift bales of hay or straw to build stacks of bales, and now – thanks to improved cleated rubber conveyor belting – to lift root crops or grain in and out of store. This Russell 90 model with 5 hp electric motor or 7 hp petrol engine has a capacity of up to 60,000 kg (60 tons) per hour. The height is adjusted by hydraulic ram, price in 1971 with 7 hp engine and 2 m (6 ft) swinging extension as shown was £815.

Silage face cutter

Keeping larger numbers of cattle to one man makes it harder to arrange self-feed barriers at the silo face. This means an automatic means of cutting out silage is needed. This W. German Mengele face cutter is reversed into the silage heap and the revolving top scraper arm works its way down the face. The cut silage falls down on to the auger at the bottom which works it to the fingers feeding the fan and blower pipe that elevates the silage into a truck designed to feed out into cattle mangers or into a complete diet feeder which will mix concentrates and straw with the silage to produce a balanced diet.

Complete diet feeding

This is a new concept of feeding cattle a balanced diet instead of over-rich or unbalanced feeds that arise when simply giving animals access to different types of fodder. Further, with the fodder broken down to small particles and thoroughly mixed it is impossible for the animals to reject less pleasant items in favour of the better parts. In the past the choosiness of animals has led to a great deal of low-quality feeds being wasted. First developed by the Oswalt company, cattle diet feeders are very popular in Italy and becoming more popular in the rest of Europe and United States. They are also useful for zero-grazing or feed-lot husbandry techniques in which the cattle remain yarded and have all their food, even fresh-cut grass, brought to their mangers daily. Spring grass is traditionally over-rich for cattle and complete diet feeders allow the farmer to tone down the rich grass with milled straw and add the necessary trace elements and vitamins to balance the diet and prevent diseases such as bloat or staggers.

MODERN TRACTORS

Fiat looks for style

The Italian Fiat company is the fifth largest tractor producer in the Western world, the leading four being International Harvester, John Deere, Massey Ferguson and Ford. Competition for world markets has led all these to offer progressively up-market ranges of tractor with better safety Q-cabs, new bonnet stylings, four-wheel-drive options as well as many features of economy or efficiency.

Other tractor builders with substantial production output are Deutz and Fendt (W. Germany), Allis-Chalmers and David Brown/Case (US owned), Renault (France), Ebro (Spain), Same/Lamborghini (Italian), Kubota and Iseki (Japan). Smaller manufacturers are Leyland (UK), White (US), Steyr (Austria), Volvo (Sweden), Valmet (Finland), Mitsubishi and Satoh (Japan), Carraro and Agrifull (Italy), Schluter and Holder (W. Germany). Picture shows Fiat 780 2wd hauling a gang of Cambridge rollers.

Ford 4100

Tractor with fully-mounted 2-furrow reversible Ransomes plough. Note the front-end jerrican-style weights added to counterbalance the see-saw effect that arises when the plough is lifted on the 3-point linkage.

Toolframe tractor by Fendt

With a more powerful engine (50 hp) than one would imagine, this specialist tractor has its own tailor-made set of toolbars designed to suit the busy market gardener or arable grower.

Is it a tractor?

The Mercedes-Benz stable includes a number of vehicles suited to the farm. Both the Unimog and the MB Trac 800 shown are good examples of the versatile range. But many authorities will not register these vehicles at Agricultural Rates or permit them to run on un-taxed diesel fuel due to the high road speed that these vehicles possess. However their rugged construction, reliable performance, front and rear 3-point linkages, 4-wheel-drive and pto options make them quite the equal of many purely farm tractors and probably indicate the way tractor design must go in the future.

The Intrac 2003 (below)

Another all-purpose vehicle rather similar to the MB Trac range, this Intrac is built by Deutz which offers a fully conventional tractor line. Here a forward control cab is fitted and the unit is also expected to carry out two jobs at a time. In this case front harrows are fitted and a sprayer on the back. Notice that the front harrows are linked on by two A-frames, one A-frame fitted to the harrow and a mating A-frame fitted to the linkage arms. This enables instant coupling and detaching to be carried out from the cab seat. The A-frame concept was invented by the Alpha-Accord company.

The big artics (right)

A distinctive feature of tractor development in the 1970s has been the emergence of big-horsepower articulated-steer tractors. Massey Ferguson, John Deere, Steiger, International Harvester, Allis-Chalmers and White artic models have been built in the United States and the Versatile in Canada. The Russian K–150 and K–300, the Czech Liaz and the Yugoslavian IMT all came on the scene within a few years. The 110 hp MF 1200 is the smallest of the MF artic range and is the only UK-built artic. It is shown powering a Carnfield rotary tiller (vertical spikes) of approximately 4 m (13 ft). A new artic (below), the 180 hp IH 3588 by International is unusual in that it features its cab on the rear 'half'.

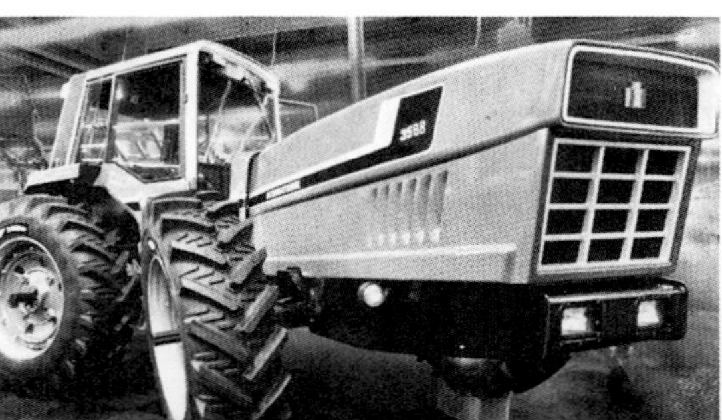

KHP 139N
MF 1200

A modern crawler tractor (below)

Crawler or 'caterpillar' tractors really had their heyday when tillage tools needed sheer lugging power. On certain flinty soils which can tear rubber tyres to shreds in no time, farmers still go for the economy of a crawler. But crawlers are limited to low speeds and lugging tasks on the farm while rubber tyres and 4-wheel-drive tractors are continually improving. For all this, there is likely to be a specialist market for tracklayers for many years to come. Principal manufacturers are Fiat, Ebro, Aveling-Marshall, Lamborghini and a number of Comecon makes.

Japanese machines (right)

Already winning large markets in the industrial tractor market with Komatsu, the Japanese turned to the agricultural sector in the 1970s. The approach was quite unexpected, that of starting production with extremely small tractors that were first considered quite toylike. From 10 to 30 hp, the Japanese manufacturers, headed by Kubota, offered machines that proved to be economical, useful and requiring little maintenance. Larger models now appearing are Iseki tractors of 50 hp-plus and a new range of 40–80 hp from Shibaura. Already the major manufacturers of Ford, Massey Ferguson, John Deere, Allis-Chalmers, and David Brown have made agreements or are considering agreements to accept Japanese-built tractors to fill the small end of their own ranges. Such supplies would be offered as the selling company's 'own make' and in 'own colours'.

KUBOTA L225
L225

Forklifts come to the farm

With so much time spent shifting supplies on the farm and seed and fertilizers now being delivered to the barn on pallets, the arrival of the farm forklift was really a forseeable event. The major tractor manufacturers have seemed unable to offer forklift versions of tractors to suit the farmer who has turned to ex-construction type forklifts for this purpose. Called rough-terrain forklifts, this latest is the Muir-Hill Four-5000 with Moovmor mast and forks.

Cleaning out a Lincolnshire ditch

A ditching jib fixed to the tractor linkage and powered by the tractor hydraulics will either dig a new ditch or clean out an existing dyke. The ditcher has stabilizer feet to keep the rig steady when slewing or reaching to bite or tip. The ditcher will complete about a metre (yard) and then must be moved on to take a new stand. The McConnel Double-D ditcher fits most tractors.

Hedging used to be a winter job (below)

When it was all hand work, hedges were usually 'laid' (entwining the saplings to grow horizontally) in the winter, and trimmed in the spring. With the advent of flail hedge trimmers (another machine using a wholly rotary action) hedges can be trimmed from the tractor seat at any time of the year. Once the hedge has been given its correct shape, it can be kept smart by flail trimmer in a fraction of the time it took by hand with a 'slashing' knife or hook. The machine shown is a Bomford Flailtrim hedgecutter driven from the tractor pto by long vee-belt. Three hydraulic rams will angle the cutter head to cut both sides of the hedge.

Continental hose drum irrigators (right)

The two drought years of 1975 and 1976 precipitated an enormous demand for irrigation machinery at a time when the mobile hose drum unit was being developed. Irrigation plant, once consisting of man-handled pipe sets, suddenly became a tractor with a pump and mobile drum like this Swedish Kaskad 75. Left on the headland, the rainer trolley is pulled into the crop as far as the unwinding hose will allow. Water pumped through the system is discharged in a wide arc by the nozzle. The water also powers a wind-in mechanism that draws the nozzle back to the drum which then switches off automatically.

Kaskad 75
Kaskad 75

Collecting stones in the field

The best variety of stone collectors are probably those made in Spain which still has much land with very many large stones close to the surface. Even back in steam plough days stones were raked to one side of a field by drawing a simple but massive rake to and fro. When the stone had collected to form a considerable quantity in the row, the raking would commence on the other side bringing stone back to join the first. Then it would be used to build a stone wall on the spot.

This stone collector by the Norwegian plough company Kvernelands shovels its way under the soil and twin elevator chains with slats across move the stone and earth up the griddled ramp. Loose earth and small stones fall back through but the larger stones are carried to the top and discharged into a side-running trailer. Stone is useful to make farm roads, especially through gateways, and to mix with cement when making concrete yards.

Doing several jobs at once

The Italian Supercoltivatrice machine consists of a powerful engine on a trailer fitted out with tanks and a seed hopper. The engine drives a pto to a 6 m (6 yd) rotary cultivator that is chopping old maize stalks into the ground and digging at the same time. Seeding harrows follow which are served by air pipes coming from the engine blower and hoppers. The air blast carries fertilizer and seed which is planted at the correct depth. Rollers follow to firm the ground while nozzles spray pesticide and pre-emergence weed killer on to the ground. All the tractor does is pull it. The tractor rear wheels are fitted with strakes – swing-out legs that lock out to give more grip on muddy ground.

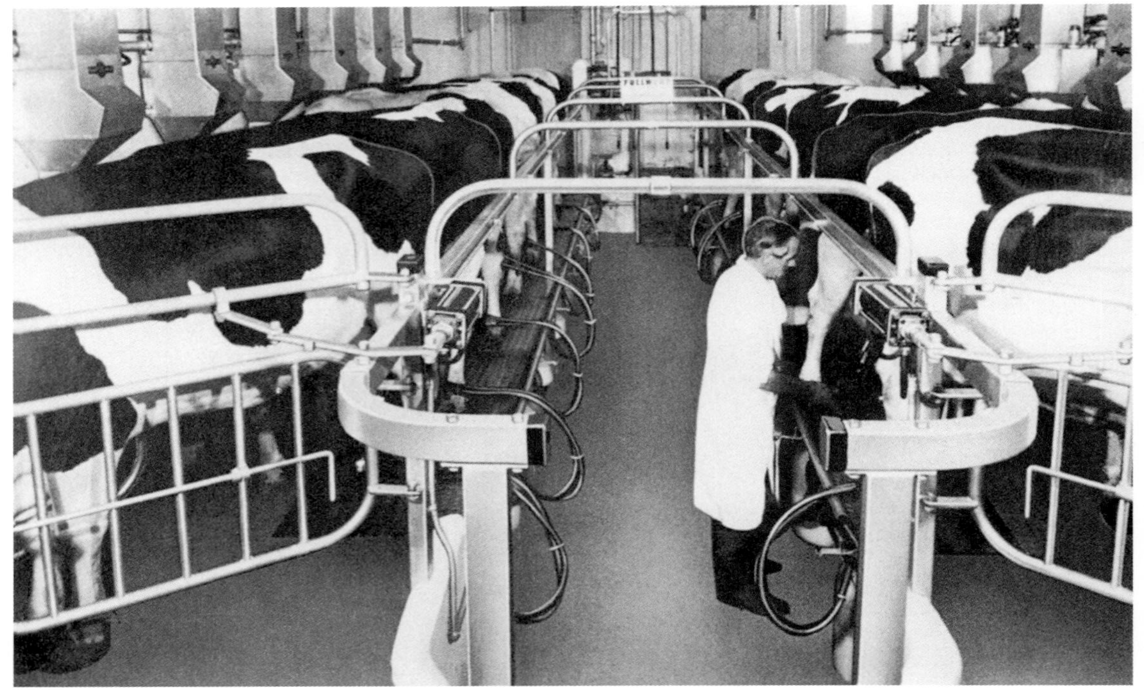

A modern herringbone milking parlour (left)

Two ranks of cattle standing slant-on to an operator working in a pit provide the 'herringbone' configuration by which this system is known. The operator deals with one side at a time, washing udders, pushing auto-feed buttons according to the cow and its milk yield, putting on the teat clusters. Then he turns to the other bank of cows which is finishing milking, takes off the teat clusters and opens the end gate for that batch of cows to walk out. He then closes the exit gate and opens the entry gate to admit another group of cows for milking, washes and feeds them and attaches the teat clusters. By this time the first bank of cows are ready to be released . . . and so on.

Close-up of operating herringbone milking parlour (below)

This parlour is a 6-a-side version and indeed the number of cows handled largely depends on whether the parlour is run by one or two operators and the degree of automation. Today it is possible to dispense with feeding concentrates (this can be done by out-of-parlour feeders controlled by mini-computer) and hand washing of udders (spray jets in preparation stalls can do this and get the cow 'letting down' her milk). There are cluster systems now that disengage and hang up automatically as milk flow ceases and all the operator need do is actually fix the cluster – a job taking about ten seconds for each cow.

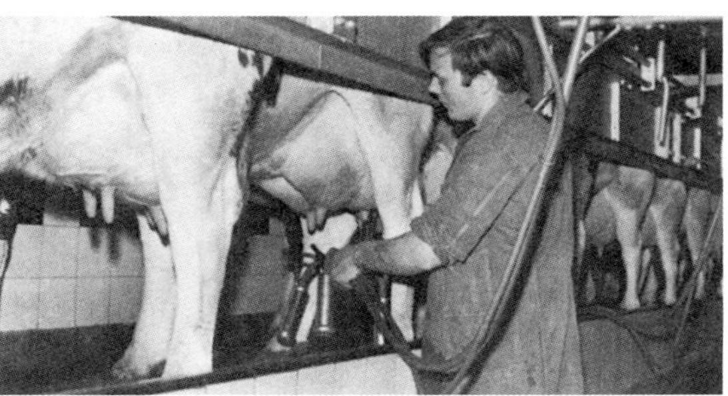

Forage towers for winter feed

Holding silage made of short-chopped grass, these towers are sometimes filled and emptied from the top, or filled at the top and emptied by a coal-cutting type of extractor at the bottom. Although expensive to install, they allow the automated feeding of cattle during the winter. The model shown is a Howard Harvestore 2080 with bottom unloader.

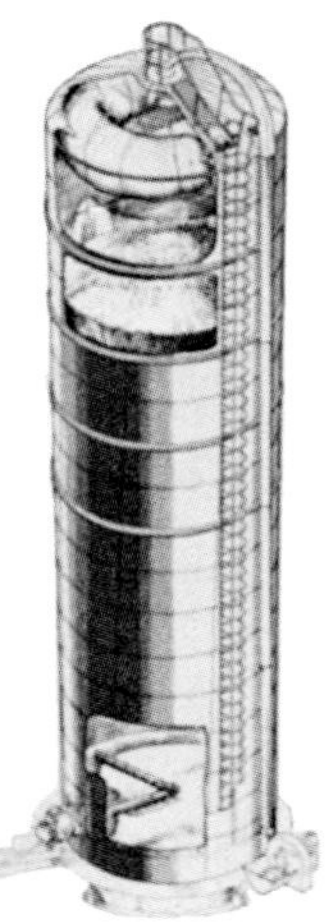

Lipp continous-strip silos

An ingenious way of making a silo is the Lipp system whereby a continous strip of metal is fed into a former set up at the base of a silo. The former folds the metal edges over in a double turn and so sets up an ever-rising spiral tube. When sufficient height is reached, the top and bottom turns are cut level and the silo is allowed to rest on the ground. The jigs and former are taken away to a new site. It is also possible to feed in a double skin, the inner layer of stainless steel, according to the commodity one intends to store.

Caustic soda straw processor

An exciting development in cattle feeding shows that straw treated with caustic soda becomes more digestible and therefore of much higher feed value. This Taarup 801 straw processor is powered by tractor pto and takes in regular oblong straw bales. These are chopped up and the straw, impregnated by caustic soda under pressure, is blown into a barn or heap to ferment for two days. It is then ready for feeding to cattle or, more usually, incorporating in complete diet feed rations or milled compound feeds. This machine has an output of 2,500 kg (2½ tons) per hour of treated straw. It needs a 70 hp tractor to power it.

Fruit-gathering canopy and tree shaker

A primitive idea but one which hasn't been improved upon in the orchards of Europe. The canopy opens in two fan-like halves, meeting around the fruit tree. The arm has a hydraulic grab that takes a firm hold of the tree trunk while a hydraulic vibrator is run. This causes the ripe fruit to fall into the canopy base which is soon emptied by hand into fruit boxes when the canopy is folded back again.

Spraying by helicopter

The picture shows a Bell 47G helicopter spraying sugar beet seedlings. Spraying by helicopter was pioneered in the 1960s and is perhaps the most promising branch of aerial farm operations. The sowing of seed and fertilizers in remote hills has been tried, also fire duty in forests and infra-red photography of crops which can spot diseases early.

Combine harvester with maize head

This Claas combine has been fitted with a different header to accept four rows of maize at once and a different threshing mechanism. The snapper head has chains that draw the maize plant through, snapping the broad corn cobs off which are taken in for threshing. The mechanisms can be replaced by a normal system to deal with cereals.

John Deere 5400 self-propelled forager

This powerful machine simply eats into any green crop, passing it through a rotor of precision chop knives on its way to the blower which fills the trailer towed at the rear. This crop of lucerne is rather special; it is being harvested for treatment at the Unitrition plant near Doncaster which extracts protein-rich grass juices now being hailed as a cheap source of protein for the future.

Precision-chop 12-knife cylinder

Typical of the cutting mechanism used in any precision chop forager, this vicious cutter is the heart of the Taarup Torrent-605 harvester.

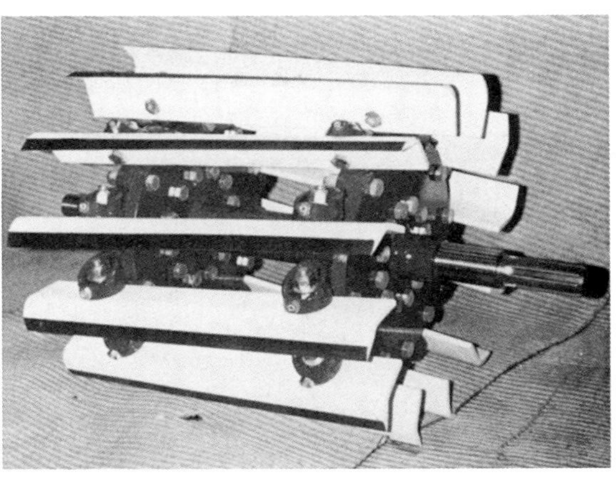

Self-propelled sprayer
Many companies are now building complete spraying units in self-propelled form. This one from the Dutch Amac company has forward-control cab and hydraulic folding boom plus many technical features to ensure an accurate application of expensive chemical sprays.

Belgian Hoes draining machine

This tracklaying drainer hauls a tough blade through the earth down which is fed a perforated plastic pipe of 7.5 cm (3 in) diameter. This will collect water and lead it off to the main drain or ditch. Although the ground may undulate, the drain is being laid on an exact level with calculated amount of fall. The tall beacon at the rear is picking up a laser beam that has been set to replicate the drain's gradient. If the tractor rises or falls, the beacon drops or lifts the drainage blade accordingly.

Different digging tackle attached to this drainer would enable it to lay a tile drain which would also be set to a level gradient by means of the laser beam control.

Orchard picker for cider or perry manufacture

As it takes fallen fruit to make cider or perry, there is no need for a tree shaker as on page **114**. This Tuthill-Temperley 721 machine has a revolving flapper to sweep all loose fruit into the machine, this is then collected on a conveyor belt that delivers it into the hopper at the rear. A powerful fan blows all the leaves and rubbish away to leave only fruit collected.

Specialist spreading machines

The 200 hp 3-wheel Terra-Gator and the 150 hp 4-wheel-drive artic-steer Ag-Gator are primarily designed to spread artificial fertilizers by contract. With 9,000 kg (9 ton) and 5,000 kg (5 ton) hoppers respectively and balloon/flotation tyres they are able to operate on wet land without bogging down. Both can be adapted to take a sprayer tank and spray boom.

FMC 2-row carrot harvester

Another specialized self-propelled machine for the vegetable world, this harvester works on the 'tops-grabbing' principle. Twin belts running down each picker grasp the plant's top foliage and haul it clear of the ground. The plant is carried up to a cutter which cuts off the root, it then falls on to the sorting, cleaning and conveying mechanism that ultimately leads to bulking in the side-running trailer. The plant top continues to the rear of the machine where the belts part to commence their return runs – leaving the unwanted leaves to fall conveniently back on to the ground. The tops-grabbing system needs good conditions to work well – the soil should be soft enough to allow the roots to be lifted out and the plant tops should be strong enough to pull the root out without tearing off.

French bean harvester

This Belgian Ploeger BP 600S French bean harvester is typical of the self-propelled machinery now entering the large market garden and canning areas. Although Belgian, this machine is now built under licence by the British company Mather & Platt.

Brussels sprouts harvester

Collecting only one row of Brussels sprout plants at a time, the grabbing elevator delivers them on to a cleated belt elevator that settles the stalk in a horizontal attitude ready for presentation to the sprout stripper that eventually sends the trimmed sprouts up into the holding tank. Not as delicate an operation as peas, nevertheless the sprouts are probably washed, packed and deep-frozen by the processing factory within four hours of being picked by this machine.

Giant pea harvester

This latest £80,000 monster Mather & Platt S8 8000 complete pea harvester can cut and lift the pea crop and extract those tender peas for freezing or canning even when the crop is wet. Unlike earlier pea viners that worked on a cut and dried crop, this machine collects the pea plants and tosses them gently in a wire drum that runs the length of its long body. The peas are extracted and gently carried to a storage hopper to await rapid collection and delivery to the processing factory. Peas have to be processed within two hours of picking or fermentation will start and spoil the tenderness.

Mather+Platt SB8000
M+P

Sidehill combine keeps level on the slopes

A last look at the familiar combine harvester shows that more improvements have taken place. This Italian Laverda M 112 AL machine not only has full hydrostatic transmission to enable the driver to choose his speed exactly, it has fully-automatic self-sensing levelling and wheel-compensating devices built into it. This enables it to harvest grain grown on hilly land; previously the combines would lose much of the grain when working in a tipped position. The header must follow the ground, of course, and demonstrates the steepness of the land. The wheels are mounted on parallelogram axles which allow one to sink and the other to rise to keep the main body of the combine level. At the same time the rear of the combine is lifted by hydraulic ram to keep it level from front to back. Most combine manufacturers offer at least one sidehill model today.

FARM MUSEUMS TO VISIT

Acton Scott Working Farm Museum
Wenlock Lodge, Acton Scott,
Church Stretton, Shropshire

Alscott Farm Museum
Shebbear, Devon

Argyll Museum of Farming Life
Auchindrain, Inveraray, Argyll

Burton Constable Hall
Sproatley, Humberside

Church Farm
Martham, Gt Yarmouth, Norfolk

Cotswold Farm Park
Guiting Power, Cheltenham, Glos.

Easton Farm Park
Easton, Woodbridge, Suffolk

Manor Farm Museum
Cogges, Nr Witney, Oxon.

Manx Open Air Museum
Cregneash, Isle of Man

Museum of English Rural Life
University of Reading,
Reading, Berkshire

Queen Elizabeth Country Park
Gravel Hill, Horndean,
Portsmouth, Hampshire

West Wales Farm Park
Blaenbedw Isaf,
Nr Llandyssul, Dyfed

It is possible to visit farms on special open days, for information write to the Association of Agriculture, Victoria Chambers, 16/20 Strutton Ground, London SW1. The Information Officer, GLC, County Hall, London SE1 and the Countryside Commission, John Dower House, Crescent Place, Cheltenham, Gloucestershire can supply details of farm trails around London and throughout the UK.

INDEX